Chapters

by Mark Falstein
illustrated by Franklin Ayers

Harcourt

Orlando Boston Dallas Chicago San Diego

Visit *The Learning Site!*

www.harcourtschool.com

Boys!

SETTING: *A sidewalk and curb, seen from the near edge of the street. Apartment building in background. A bus stop and bench stand at center. Now and then we hear the sound of passing cars.*

AT RISE: GWEN *is sitting on the bench, reading a book. JACKY enters left. He is riding a skateboard. He jumps off the board, flipping and catching it. He looks uncertainly at GWEN. Did she see his trick or not? She glances at him and sees him watching her. Then she goes back to her reading, holding the book close to her face.*

JACKY (*Stepping off of his skateboard*): Hi.

GWEN (*Not looking up*): Hi.

(JACKY, *trying to appear casual, crosses in front of* GWEN *and sits to her left. He tries to see the cover of her book, but* GWEN *holds it against her body.*)

GWEN (*Annoyed*): Do you mind?

JACKY: Hey, I only wanted to see what you're reading.

GWEN: Jacky, I realize this is a public school bus stop, but that doesn't give you the right to invade my privacy.

JACKY (*Backing off quickly*): Well, excuse me! What's the big deal? Everyone reads that Scared Stiff series. It's really cool.

GWEN (*Returning to her book*): Yes, isn't it?

(JACKY *throws a scowl at her. SKIP enters right. At the same time,* DELIA *enters right.* SKIP *taps* JACKY *on the shoulder.* JACKY *looks up, startled.* GWEN *again clutches her book and then relaxes as the two boys greet each other.*)

JACKY: Hey, Skipster!

SKIP: Hey, Jacky! Where have you been all summer?

(SKIP *comes around the right side of the bench. He and* JACKY *give each other "high fives." During the following dialogue,* DELIA *looks at the boys uncertainly.*

JACKY: Oh, you know. Riding my board. Mostly I bustled around making deliveries for my mom's store. You?

SKIP: Oh, you know, stuff. Swimming. Tennis. Practicing with my band.

JACKY: You're in a band?

SKIP: Oh, didn't you know? "The Sleepless Knights." Get it? Knights? Like in chess?

JACKY: Cool. What kind of music do you play?

SKIP (*Evasively*): Oh, you know. Rock and roll, a little country. (*He plays an imaginary guitar.*)

JACKY: Hey, I didn't know you played guitar. Is music going to be your elective at Woodside?

New School, New World

SKIP: I don't know. Maybe. What's an elective? (JACKY *looks at him in disbelief.* SKIP *laughs.*) Just kidding. I haven't decided. Music, drama, wood shop, Chinese. Too many choices. New school, new world, know what I mean?

JACKY: Yes, I do know. (*Shakes his head*) I thought the first day of middle school would never come, but here it is. Not that I was worried about it, of course. (JACKY *smiles confidently and flexes his muscles.*) I just hope Woodside is ready for me and all my charm!

SKIP: (*Laughing a little*) You'll be a big hit, all right. I bet all the ninth grade girls will be begging you to talk to them. (*Snickers*)

SKIP: (*Turns to the girls.*) Hi, Gwen.

GWEN (*Looks up briefly and smiles*): Hi.

SKIP: (*Points at her book*) Hey, what are you reading? School hasn't even started yet!

JACKY: Watch it, Skip. You're invading her privacy. (*He offers GWEN another scowl.*) As if I haven't known her since kindergarten or anything.

GWEN (*Under her breath*): Some boys act like they're still *in* kindergarten.

JACKY: Who, me?

GWEN: I wasn't talking to you!

SKIP: Whoa, did I miss something here?

JACKY: Ask her!

SKIP (*Sitting down next to* GWEN): This is Gwen Barnes, right? Ms. Let's-Have-a-Party? The quickest point guard in the sixth grade?

GWEN (*Quietly*): We're not in sixth grade any more.

SKIP: Really? So how did you spend your summer vacation? Deciding to dump on all your friends so you could make all new ones?

GWEN: I spent it putting aside childish things! (*She tries to put the book in her backpack. Another book inside the backpack falls out onto the street. She lunges for it, but SKIP reaches it first. He looks at the cover.*)

SKIP: *Travels in Italy?*

GWEN (*Sheepishly*): Will you give me my book, please?

SKIP (*Opening the book*): "Museums and galleries of Florence?" "Where to stay in Venice?" Your family's going to Italy?

GWEN: Yes! I mean, no! I'm just reading about it. Is that a problem for you, Mr. Rock-and-Roll Star?

DELIA: Italy is lovely. I hope you do get there. (*Everyone turns and looks at DELIA.*)

GWEN: You've been to Italy?

A Beam of Light

DELIA: Every summer since I was six. My dad lives there.

JACKY: Cool. And your mom lives here?

DELIA: No, I live with my grandmother. (*For a moment, she looks upset, but she quickly recovers.*) Italy is wonderful, Gwen. If it's your conviction that you should go there, I'm sure you'll be propelled to Italy on a beam of light!

(*The others look at DELIA strangely for a moment.*)

GWEN: Well, an airplane's safer. What's your name?

DELIA: Delia. (*She nods to the boys.* JACKY, *flustered, takes out his skateboard and begins rocking.*)

GWEN: (*Ignoring the boys, especially* JACKY) I'm Gwen. Are you starting middle school today, too?

DELIA: (*Looking a little nervous*) Yes. We just moved here last week. My grandma's still unpacking. (*She shades her eyes and looks down the street for the school bus.*) Shouldn't the bus be here by now?

GWEN: Yeah, but don't worry. It's always late on the first day. Where in Italy does your Dad live?

DELIA: Well, he lives in Rome, but he travels a lot on business. He works for a big international company that's based in Rome. Siena, Milan, Naples—he and I have traveled all over Italy. Every summer we spend a week visiting another country, too. Last summer we went to France.

SKIP: Hey, we studied ancient Rome last year.

GWEN: Skip, she doesn't care!

SKIP: Hey, what's got into you? First you're mad at Jacky and now me. (*Handing her the book with a scowl*) Here. Have a nice trip.

(*He turns away. GWEN stares at the book, looks at SKIP, and then slowly returns the book to her backpack.*)

Expressing Yourself

DELIA (*Breaking the silence*): Skip, I heard you say that drama is an elective at Woodside?

SKIP: Yeah.

DELIA: Do they do real plays, or do they just, you know, do kid things?

SKIP (*Looking at her*): Well, my big sister was in *Romeo and Juliet* there last year. Is that real enough for you?

DELIA: (*Quickly*) That's fine. That's wonderful. I didn't mean to insult your school—our school. I just want to be in a drama program that will let me express myself. I heard you mention your band, too, Skip. Tell me about it—the Sleepless Knights. Could I come and hear you play sometime?

SKIP (*Sheepishly*): Well, it's not exactly a band yet.
(JACKY *tries not to laugh and ends up snorting instead.*)
DELIA: (*Pretending not to notice* JACKY) I understand.
You're just getting started.
SKIP (*Glaring at* JACKY): Well, I wouldn't exactly say that,
either. Right now, it's more like an idea that a couple of
us have. (*With a flourish*) But if we have conviction, we'll
be propelled to the top of the charts on a beam of light!
(SKIP and JACKY *laugh.* DELIA *joins in but is clearly embar-
rassed.* GWEN, *not laughing, gives* SKIP *a disgusted look.*)

DELIA: (*Looking down*) I guess I express myself too strongly sometimes.

GWEN: That's okay! I guess we all do sometimes. (*They all sit quietly for a minute; then GWEN turns to the boys.*) I'm sorry, Skip. You too, Jacky. I'm sorry about how I talked to you. I guess I'm just nervous about starting middle school today. I'm worried that everyone will think I'm still a little kid.

JACKY (*After a pause*): It's cool, Gwen.

SKIP: Forget it, Gwen. I think we're all a little worried about being the youngest kids in the school. I liked it a lot better in sixth grade, when we were the oldest!

JACKY: (*Nodding*) Me, too!

GWEN: You know what I was just thinking? Some teacher today is going to ask me to write "How I Spent My Summer Vacation." (*To* SKIP) "New school, new world," right? But the same old stuff!

JACKY: You know what could be cool? If a teacher asks us to write "How I *Wish* I Had Spent My Summer Vacation!" (*They laugh.*)

GWEN: Oh, here's the bus!

(*During the following dialogue, all gather their things and form a line. Lights begin to fade.*)

SKIP: Hey, Delia. Welcome to the neighborhood!

DELIA: Thank you. It's great to meet you all.

GWEN: And please tell me all about Italy!

(*Sound of a bus approaching. The curtain falls.*)